In Search of Hallelujahs

By Jean-Bertho Almonord

DORRANCE PUBLISHING CO
EST. 1920
PITTSBURGH, PENNSYLVANIA 15238

Dorrance Publishing Co
585 Alpha Drive
Pittsburgh, PA 15238
Visit our website at www.dorrancebookstore.com

ISBN: 978-1-6461-0164-1
eISBN: 978-1-6461-0707-0

INTRODUCTION

When I started writing this book, I was in a low point in life. I was homeless. I did not have access to money. I was going from shelter to shelter. Most people thought that I was a junkie finished with life. I am not a junkie. I don't do drugs. I am not a thief. Yet my entire life seemed like I was under a curse from God. Why do good people go through these intense periods of trials and sufferings? We probably will never know.

The first title for this book was Hallelujah for a mountainous man. However, my manuscripts were stolen and someone patented the title; in effect, I had to change the title. The new title for this book came from a title of a book that I started writing titled In Search of Social Mobility: my second written book. The title spoke to me in ways I do not know. There is a disconnect between the two titles: one is about searching for a spiritual thing; the other is about searching for a more tangible thing. For example, why do people go on searching for things that are spiritual? it seems that only God deserves Hallelujahs. However, the term Hallelujah means praise be to God. If anything, people can go in search of praise be to God after they have done exceptional feats. In fact, this encourages the title In search of hallelujahs.

The protagonist of this book is Jean. He is very ingenuous and beats death at its game many times in life. He gets the well deserved hallelujah in the title of the book because of his resourcefulness. Whenever Jean is faced with a problem, he comes with a clever solution. If he cannot come up with a clever solution, he looks up to God for a solution.

The book takes place in Northern Haiti, Saint-Louis du Nord. The name of the town translated into english is Saint-Louis of the North. It begs the question that if there is a Saint-Louis of the North, is there a Saint-Louis of the South. Yes, there is also a Saint-Louis of the South in Haiti. Saint-Louis of the North is situated in between the two famous towns of Port-de-paix and Le Cap Haitien. There is also ile de la tortue also known as Tortuga Island nearby.

The town is a town consisting mostly of grimeaux, light skinned Haitians. There are mulatres and negs as well. The grimeaux are the light skinned Haitians. The mulatres are the mulattoes Haitians. The negs are the dark skinned Haitians. Even though the mulatres hold economic control of the nation; it is said that the grimeaux are a more powerful caste. There are very few whites living in the nation. Furthermore, the Taino blood have been wiped out. Some people have Taino features that are apparently strong, but they only remember their history from the history books. They know that Haiti's Taino name is Quisqueya Bohio. Its original name is Aiti. After the Haitian revolution, an H was added to breathe life into the nation as a new world nation: a western nation versus an eastern nation. The nation had changed its name effectively from Saint Domingue to Haiti. Saint-Domingue is the name given to the island by France. Furthermore, the entire physical island, including the Dominican republic, is named Hispaniola. Haiti was never Hispaniola; It lost the Hispanic identity when the French colonized the island.

At any rate, the story unfolds with Jean going through the many different stages of christianity and the occult as a peon. He became a saint and is no longer a peon Christian. However to the rest of his family, he is a peon. The story unfolds beautifully. It is my sincere hope that everyone who starts this book will also finish it.

CHAPTER 1

J ean was born in St. Louis-du-Nord, Haiti. The name of the town translated into English is Saint Louis of the North. As the name suggest, this town is located in the northern part of Haiti. There are surrounding towns such as Port-de-paix, translated to the Port of peace, and Le Cap Haitien, translated to the Haitian Cape. St-Louis-du-Nord is a small town of farmers; the economy is agrarian. There are some little shops here and there, however it is not a big town. It is also mountainous; it has a lot of mountains. A good part of the town does not even have electricity. The story takes place around the year 1981.

Around that period of time, Haiti was under the Duvalier dictatorship. There were curfews. The military had total control of the nation. There were constant beatings of the citizens. People would get arrested for no reason and then no one would hear from them. The rights of most Haitians were restricted during that regime.

Haiti is a majority catholic nation. Roman catholicism is alive and well. People believe in the trinity: that God exists as the Father, the Son, and the Holy Spirit. They believe in the virgin birth. They believe that there are saints in the church; they also believe Saint

Marie is one of the chief saints of the church. They are under the spiritual leadership of the pope.

Over in the mountains, there was a woman named Sofiana. She was pregnant with a baby and she didn't want her parents to know. It was her first child and the child was out of wedlock. The society was a society of appearances. When the parents found out, they had to save face that their daughter was having a child out of wedlock. They wondered as to the fate of the child; they wondered as to whether Sofiana could raise him as a single parent; they had well-merited fears and qualms. They decided to give Sofiana the advice to abort the child.

Their plans to abort the child was not only in terms of Sofiana. They feared whether anyone would muster the courage to ask Sofiana's hand in marriage.They feared that she would be heavily dependent upon them. Sofiana's parents are Jean-Paul and Ana Lapierre.

The next day, Sofiana went on her way to the markets to buy a plant that would have done the abortive job. She bought the plant and decided she would go on with the silent murder. Meanwhile, lies a man alone who was clueless about the fate of his future son. One could have said that just maybe that he didn't know that he had a future son on the way; however,even if Sofiana didn't tell him; he still had no excuse. It is funny how the men are sometimes left out of these proceedings. However, these men are accountable for anything that occurs to their children; they were an accomplice to the birth; they are just as much an accomplice to the death of the child.

Jean-Bertho Almonord

Sofiana made a concoction with the abortive leaves. Shen then drank it. Nothing occured after the first thirty minutes. Nothing occured after the first hour. It wasn't until after the second hour that the concoction kicked in. At this point, her body temperature rose. She gained a severe stomach ache. The baby started to kick inside the womb. The baby started to cry, She then began to experience birth pangs, and the baby screamed out in baby talk that only the mother could understand, "I am coming out alive." This is how Sofiana gave birth to Jean. This was Jean's first struggle with death as an innocent baby and he had prevailed. Jean had earned his first hallelujah for prevailing over death as a newborn infant.

Sofiana named the baby Jean. She also gave him the nickname ti Jean in the Haitian Creole spoken in the North of Haiti; it is a creole that is somewhat different than the creole spoken throughout the rest of Haiti. Ti Jean is short for the French petit Jean. It translates into English as little Jean. She put an amulet around the child to protect him.

Was Sofiana a protestant? No, Sofiana was catholic. As a catholic, she believed in amulets. She believed they had protective powers to protect and provide for her child. She believed that it was her duty as a mother to watch and provide for her child: the best way to do it would be with an amulet according to her.

In Haiti, protestantism is shunned. Most people do not like the protestants. The Catholics view them as judgmental and annoying. Their churches are loud and people dance everywhere; whereas in the catholic sphere, churches are quiet and orderly. The protestants are always saying that they are the only Christians and that the Catholics are not christians. Most of the protestants feign not to know what a saint is, although the word itself is written in the Bible many times: they believe that a saint is a statue that Catholics worship. They do acknowledge that the Catholics and the protestants share the same Bible. The protestants are proud and say things like the Catholics are illiterate and that they do not read their Bibles. It is true that the rate of illiteracy is very high in Haiti, yet the illiteracy rate is shared between both sects of Christianity.

Several months after Jean's birth, he went through baptism. This was merely a consecration of Jean into Catholicism. Sofiana is Catholic and she chose Catholicism for Jean. This kind of consecration dedicates the life of the child to Jesus Christ. The hope is that he will live and choose God. It is also a protective consecration. The consecration hopes to protect the child with Jesus against the high rate of infant mortality that is prevalent in the world.

Most people do not know what Catholicism is. They think it is a dead sect of Christianity; to their amazement, Catholicism has always been alive and doing well. Christianity was established with the death, burial, and resurrection of Jesus. Jesus is usually referred to as Jesus Christ, in which Christ means the anointed one. In effect people are saying Jesus the anointed one when they say Jesus Christ. Furthermore, a Christian is a follower of Christ, or one belonging to Christ. After the early church was established, the Bible was written in order to guide all christians into all doctrines and truths. The church grew and many people were receptive to Christianity and accepted Christ as their personal savior. Christianity became a powerhouse. Three centuries later, many Christians were giving their lives as martyrs for Christ. A Roman emperor named

Constantine legalized Christianity and decreed a law that the church is Catholic and is universal; it means that there is one church and that church is Catholic. Catholicism is older than protestantism.

It is funny how the majority of Haiti is Catholic. The approximate percentage is higher than eighty percent. How did this come about? Haiti is in the Caribbean close to North America: a protestant hub. Jamaica, Trinidad, the Bahamas, and the majority of the smaller islands are protestant. The only other Catholic nation in the Caribbean environment is the Dominican Republic. Furthermore with America and Canada in North America as the two economic powerhouses as protestant nations, it makes one wonder why Haiti continuingly chooses the Catholic route.

One has to look at the history of Haiti to see why it is a Catholic nation. The island Hispaniola which Haiti shares with the Dominican Republic was colonized by the Spaniards. After a while, the French wanted half of the island as a colony because it was too prosperous; Hispaniola had one of the biggest slave economies; it was mainly a sugarcane economy. Around 1697, a treaty was passed that divided the island into two: the treaty of Ryswick. The French owned the western one third of the island; the Spaniards owned the Eastern two thirds of the island. The entire island Hispaniola also goes by the name Santo Domingo. After the division of the island, the French part came to be known as Saint Domingue; the Spanish part retained the name Santo Domingo. This name is confusing because if one were speaking French, how would one refer to Santo Domingo, but as Saint Domingue.

When the Spaniards and the French went to colonize, they went under the auspices of their respective monarchy and catholicism; the Catholic Church placed a blessing on them. As a result, these colonizers imposed Catholicism on the locals; Some accepted heartily; others accepted begrudgingly. As a result, that is the reason why Haiti and the Dominican republic are two Catholic nations in the Caribbean.

CHAPTER 2

Sofiana was very attentive to her child. She watched him grow with intense curiosity. Jean was now at the age of two. She always thought about what he would amount to in life. She met with the father at another point in time, and revealed to him that he had a son. He said that he simply didn't care. It is an unfair mystery when a man shirks all the responsibility of raising a child on a woman. At the heart of the matter, lies the fact that the father of the child did not even care to share the fact that he had a son with his family. Some family members might have been kind hearted and show love to the child; some would even dare to bring the child gifts. Some would even dare to bring the family to meet the child, albeit behind the unapproving father's back.

The child grew in wisdom and stature and in favor with God and men. He learned how to talk at the age of two. He couldn't talk as clearly as a grown man, however he talked fine for a two year old. He started crawling at the age of one, and by the age of two, he could fully walk. However, Sofiana kept looking at his face to see an imprint of his father and she saw none. She wondered; she had often heard people say that some children start resembling their parents at the later years in life. She hoped that he would resemble both parents.

Jean had Sofiana's roundish face. He also had her hazel green eyes. He was lightskin. He had a normal black person's hair. He had a handsome physique for a two year old. However, Sofiana kept asking herself, when would Jean's father's traits start to show. At a deeper level, what she had been trying to say to herself is that the child has two parents; they both need to be involved; they both need to love the child; they both need to support the child with any areas of his life that he needs help in.

One day Jean was walking in the backyard of the house unattended. There was a basin of water nearby. These basins are used to keep the house fresh. They serve as a source of drinking water as well as bathing water. Jean was walking and inadvertently fell into the water basin. As a child, he started screaming. Sofiana was not at home at the time. A cousin of Sofiana's named Mariana scurried off to the water basin. She jumped in and grabbed Jean and thereby rescued him. That was the second time that Jean had prevailed over death; the first time, he prevailed over an abortive death; the second time, he prevailed over an aquatic death. One says hallelujah for Jean for prevailing over death a second time at such a young age.

CHAPTER 3

When Jean turned four, Sofiana decided to muster the courage to have a real talk with the father of Jean, whose name was Joseph. The conversation they had was as follow.

Sofiana: How is it going Joseph?

Joseph: I am fine as usual.

Sofiana: You do know why I am here?

Joseph: I think it's about the little bastard. Please make this quick. I don't have time to waste.

Sofiana: Well, your son is now four. His name is Jean. He is starting to look more and more like you. We are having a little birthday party for him. We would like to invite you and some members of your family to the party.

Joseph: No

Sofiana: why not? It would be nice.

Joseph: I don't really care. That little bastard is not mine. You will not tie me down to a life of pernury. I have plans.

Sofiana: Joseph, your son needs major help from you. He is just a child. He didn't ask to be born. You can at least pretend to care and show up.

Joseph: good bye!

Sofiana felt like crying after realizing that Joseph was not interested in raising Jean with her. She pondered on the meaning of love and how love could be so unrequited. A baby deserves love from both parents. Unrequited love is one of the worst things. To love someone and to have them not love you back in return is simply wrong, she thought. Furthermore, there were two persons who should love Jean: Sofiana and possibly Joseph. She was not sure if she could include Joseph; however, she felt that if the child was loved by his father, then the child would simply show Joseph love in return.

It is a confusing thing how love works? Is love a virtue, an emotion, or a power. One might not be sure which of these categories, love falls in. However, one can be sure that love is something that can be felt. It means that Joseph can sense that Sofiana is in love with him, but he is uninterested. If love can be felt, then one can respond back to the love that he/she has felt. When one responds back to the love that one has felt, love is said to be loyal. It is not readily apparent that one can be faithful to love. However, with

Jean-Bertho Almonord

babies and children, one can think that the love shown to them, that exceeds the normal love that a parent is supposed to show a child, might point to the fact that parents are being faithful to their child; love can be said to be faithful.

The birthday party occured. None of Joseph's family including Joseph showed up. It was horrible for Sofiana. She cried throughout the party. However, Jean turned five. There were many people there. There was a little sugary cake called a gateau in Haitian creole. Jean enjoyed the gateau very much. Jean will start going to school this year; he is looking forward to attending school.

CHAPTER 4

At this point in time, Jean turned seven. Seven is one of these ages, in which most people go through a transition. Jean went through many transitions at this age. One day when Jean was getting ready for bedtime, Sofiana decided to share with Jean the story of Joseph: hoping that one day Jean and Joseph would be reconciled. Joseph would love Jean and Jean would love Joseph in return. Jean then asked her, "is this why all of my friend's dads are always around and my dad is never around." She replied 'yes.' She then told him that one day she would take him to see Joseph; Jean was happy to hear that fact.

At this point, Jean was a bit tall and linky for his age. He was starting to look more like his dad too. Joseph also had a roundish face; one is not sure why Sofiana would think that Jean looks more like her than his dad. His dad's eyes were brown unlike his mom's eyes that were green.

Sofiana mustered up her strength and took Jean to see Joseph. She said to herself, "in the event that Joseph is not home, she would present him to the family. She would deal with the repercussions afterward. They reached Joseph's house and he was home. Joseph answered the door and he realized that Jean was there. He was angered and gave her a really mean look. He then said to her "what is this bastard doing here?" Joseph's mother who heard the word bastard ran to the door to see who it was. She flustered when she saw Jean. She said to Joseph, 'but he looks just like you." Joseph responded "it doesn't matter, I don't want a child. I can't even take care of myself now and you two would like for me to take care of this child. I am staying away from the child." Joseph's mother's name was Matilde. Sofiana cried to Matilde, "I only want Joseph to be involved in the life of this child. I do not even require financial assistance though I am poor. Matilde retorted,"You seem to think I don't know what you women are about, ruin a man's life forever with a baby. Furthermore, who tells me that this is Joseph's child." Sofiana felt like crying. Jean started to weep. He was only seven, but he knew that it was sheer humiliation for him and his mother Sofiana. Joseph yelled, "get away from my house." Sofiana took Jean by the hand and left right away.

Sofiana cried for days after this incident. She wondered why Joseph didn't want to get to know his child. She also wondered if there was another woman in the picture. She decided to talk to her father and mother. Jean-Paul and Ana told her some haitian advice. Her father said to her, "you are catholic, you need to start taking your son to church. Furthermore, if you want to find out if he has another woman, you know where to find out. Simply don't be so mean to the other woman." Ana agreed and said, "your father has given you sound advice, please listen to him." It might seem that this advice is far-fetched; however, Jean-Paul and Ana knew what they were talking about.

Jean-Bertho Almonord

That night, Sofiana told Jean that she would be going to see Mariana and possibly sleep over. She went to see an occultic voodoo lord. The voodoo lord consulted the occultic realm and revealed to her that Joseph had two other women. Both of which he loved more than her. He then told her that they were trying to kill Jean, These nightmares that Jean has been having are due to these women. He then told her that I give you ten days to bring Jean for protection. She paid the voodoo lord and said thank you.

Ten days later, she returned with Jean. Jean was scared; It was his first time in such a place. He remained quiet. Until the voodoo lord spoke to him and said that you have "two women who want to kill you and your mother. You have the right to avenge your mother." Jean remained silent. Afterwards, Jean was made to drink alcohol and blood. He was to made to jump over a little fire and then he went home with his mom.

That same night, a spirit appeared in front of Jean in his sleep and revealed to him that Joseph's mother Matilde would die in three days of cancer. The next day, Jean called his mom on the side and revealed to her the dream. He asked her, "could it be true?" She said to him if the spirits told you that, then it must be so. In three days, Matilde died of cancer.

On sunday, Jean went to mass at La Sainte Marie. The mass was very orderly. Jean went and spoke to the priest. The priest asked him, "do you remember me, Jean?" Jean responded, "I don't know you." Then he said "I baptized you as a baby. You were consecrated in the catholic church. I wanted you as an altar boy. Do you know that once a catholic always a catholic." He smiled, then he went away. Jean then asked his mom, what an altar boy was? She responded that altar boys are helpers to the priests.

The boy continued to grow in the physical and in intelligence. He loved going to school and learning. He also loved going to church. Yet, he had much to learn about this world before he gets his next hallelujah.

CHAPTER 5

Jean turned ten. He then started to help with the farming. The first crop that his grandfather, Jean-Paul, taught him how to plant was corn. The whole concept is that one places several corn stalks in his/her hand. One then dig a small hole in the ground and place the stalks in all the holes. Jean never quite understood why he couldn't plant just one stalk at a time and get result. The answer is that some stalks die while others live. He learned how to plant them in formation. He also learned that corn is a resilient crop; it doesn't need much water to grow. He then learned how to plant beans. He learned that grains are planted the same way that corn is planted. He later learned how to plant plantains, yucca, ginger, yams, sugarcane, avocadoes, coffee, cacao, peanut, breadfruit, okra, parsley , papaya, mangoes, quenepes, carrots, garlic, parsley, beets, eggplants, onions, and green onions. He learned that there was at least three types of yams, yam guinen (a grayish yam), yam seguine (a yellow yam), and yam mabidi (a whitish yam). He learned that there are multiple types of plantains such as: banan (regular plantains), figue (small roundish plantains) , and kiyez (short and fat plantains). After learning these lessons, Jean was well on his way of becoming a farmer. Jean had earned another hallelujah; he could have a trade in which to sustain himself and his family.

It is funny how in the provinces that most people live off a diet of roots, plants, and meats in general : whereas in the capital most people live off of a diet of rice and beans and meat in general. Most people in Jean's family do not like rice; they simply do not enjoy eating it. After school and especially on the weekends, Jean tended the gardens in the small lot of land that his family possessed. He would water the gardens. After watering the gardens, he would pick the crops that are ripe.

The temperature in the North of Haiti is good for plant growth. Plants grow well in such a warm climate. Jean came to realize that the family lived and sustained themselves off their lands; as in if they don't produce crops, they starve.

Jean's training continued from his grandfather, Jean-Paul. He learned how to cultivate and grow pigs, chicken, pintades (a guinea fowl), goats, and cows, ducks, and pigeon birds. He also learned how to catch fish such as red snappers, yellow snappers, and orange snappers. Jean was taught how to kill these animals. One kills these animals by cutting the head off first by the throat. Jean learned how to preserve these meats after the killing and deboning of the animal; one preserved them with salt. Jean learned how to make peanut butter. One uses a machine with a lever that one rotates with the hands. As one rotates it, it applies a force crushing the peanuts. It is too be noted that a little oil and salt is added to the peanut butter. Jean had earned another hallelujah for at least learning these things; one day he would be self sufficient in life.

Jean-Bertho Almonord

Jean would watch Sofiana and Ana cook and prepare the meals. Well, he thought that it would be fun to learn. So he asked his mom, "how come grandpa doesn't help with the cooking?" His mom responded that "he is too busy." His grandma responded, "cooking is a woman's business, farming and raising the animals are man's businesses." Jean was very perceptive and he asked, "may I help, and they responded no." He then decided that I will learn how to cook by watching over the women and engaging them in conversation as they are cooking. Jean earned another hallelujah for learning a bit about society and cooking.

At school, Jean excelled in all his subjects. In Haiti, school work is graded on a scale of 1 to 10. 5 or below being failure, and 10 being excellence. If five or below can denote failure, there must be lower levels of failure that counts in the Haitian school system. At school, Jean was in one classroom all day. There he learned grammar, math, French, science, geography, and history. Jean didn't have a reading class, he read for all of his classes, so it wasn't a requirement. Jean's notes in school were usually tens and nines. For maintaining an attitude of excellence in his schoolings, Jean earns another hallelujah; He has a good head on his shoulders.

The Haitian school grade system is based on the French grade system. The grade levels in school are as follow: Kindergarten, preparatoire, elementaire, moyen, and more. For the aforementioned grades there are always two levels as in Moyen 1 and Moyen 2. Each one is a year of schooling. At the age of ten, Jean was in elementaire 2. After school, He would use the didactic way of learning. His mom would ask him, what is the history of Haiti? He would respond in a song, the history of Haiti is the study of the past of Haiti. She would ask him, what is geography? He would respond geography is the study of the earth and its inhabitants. She would ask him what is French grammar? French grammar is a grouping of rules for writing and speaking French correctly. After he felt that he knew the material well enough, he would move on to something else.

Jean-Bertho Almonord

CHAPTER 6

Jean turns thirteen. At that age, Jean became a bit obnoxious. He was less interested in school, farming, and spying on the women in his family's cooking. He started searching for a deeper philosophical meaning to life at a shallow level. At school, some girls started showing interest in Jean. Instead of saying, I will continue to keep my head on my shoulder. He caved to those girl's desires. He would meet with them after school. One of those girl's name was Vernice. He was even sexually active with the girl; he is fortunate that his grandfather gave him money for contraceptives.

He was never comfortable talking to his mother about the girls and sex. He always went to talk to his grandfather about these issues. He was growing in wisdom because he knew the fact that most women do not like to talk to men about these issues. His grandfather gave him some great advice. He told him that I cannot tell you not to have sex, but I can tell you to be safe and use contraceptives. He also told him that raw sex might feel more sensuous but safe sex is more thoughtful. With safe sex, one is thinking about his/her future; one is thinking about not overpopulating the earth and preserving one's lineage through a proper marriage.

There are guys who were Jean's age that had two or three babies. His grandfather's advice was crucial in giving him a respectful manly mindset.

It is quite obvious that a good male role model in a child's life makes a great difference in the decisions that the child will make later on. Furthermore, sound advice has a great impact on all people. The advice given to Jean by Jean-Paul is sound advice. It solidifies Jean-Paul as the positive male role model in Jean's life.

One day, Jean decided to go to the local club called a balle in Haitian Creole. He went with Vernice. The whole point of the club is that males and females dance together holding hands. While at the club, he saw Joseph with a very beautiful women named Darnelle. He was sitting down eating with her. Joseph hadn't even noticed Jean. It is probably because Jean grew and was less noticeable. As the older couple were sitting there, another beautiful women came yelling at the both of them. Her name was Martique. Here is the conversation.

Martique: How could you do this to me?

Joseph: How could I do what?

Martique: now I know that you are a dead dog. Your son is here and you don't even know.

Joseph: what? Who brought this little dumbo here?

Martique: Here he is dancing with a pretty girl

Joseph got up and walked straight to Jean and said 'get out.' Jean retorted that "you do not tell me what to do, you are not my dad. From the last time I checked, I paid.". Joseph responded "Stop playing fresh with me, I did bring you into this world."

Within seconds Jean was knocked out on the floor from a punch that Joseph gave him. The owner appeared and said to Jean that "Joseph is a bigger client than you are." "Please stop coming to my balle." "Go to another one!" Jean felt like crying because the nearest balle is in another town, the town of Port-de-paix.

At home, Jean told his mom, Sofiana, what happened. Sofiana was shocked. She asked him stubbornly, "did Joseph really punch you? What a brute?" He responded, 'yes.' "The point is that I have to go to another balle," He told his mom. She said that "the nearest one is in Port-de-paix. I have a cousin who lives there. Her name is Merlande. You can probably stay at her house if it gets too late in the balle. I just need to ask her."

Sofiana then went into her room and reflected on the course of events that took place. She decided that if Joseph can have two women, she could surely date again. Love compels one to do the strangest things.

Two weeks later, Sofiana was dating a guy named Ricardo. He was a faux-grimo. He had a parent in the grimeau caste and a parent in the neg caste. This is equivalent to having one light skinned parent and one dark skinned parent. Ricardo was a handsome, medium build, averaged height guy. He always had one joke that all Haitians are Ricardoes. No one knew what he meant by that. Everyone simply smiled when he said it.

Sofiana and Ricardo decided to go to the balle on a Saturday night. To Sofiana's surprise, Joseph was not there. She wanted to see Joseph and the other two women as well. She did not see them. Sofiana and Ricardo were sitting as a couple. She kept looking over her shoulders for Joseph. At one point Ricardo became disinterested. He noticed that she was doing that. He asked her, "were you here for someone else? "She abruptly responded 'no.'

Sofiana needed to reaccustom herself back to the dating life. At her tender age of 31, most people would think that it would be easy. It was difficult for her. She had stop dating after the birth of Jean. Furthermore, she found herself nitpicking everything that Ricardo does. She later spoke on that subject with her mother: Ana. Ana gave her some great advice along the lines that nitpicking is not always a bad thing. If it occurs too often, it might be a sign that you are not in love with him.

What about Sofiana's family? What caste were they in? They were all grimeaus and grimelles. Some looked like they were mulatres (mulattoes). Even Jean was a grimeau. What about Joseph's family? They were grimeaus and grimelles as well.

How does this caste play into Haitian society? There are entire sections of a town that is neg, grimeau, or mulatres. People of the same caste congregate and live among themselves. In the mountains, where Jean is from, the majority of those living there are grimeaux. The highest caste is the mulatres, then the middle castes

Jean-Bertho Almonord

is the grimeaux caste, last but not least is the neg caste. Haiti is a majority poor nation; Most grimeaux and negs are poor. The gross national income is two dollars per day. The mulatres control most of the economy; they own most of the businesses.

Jean noticed that with the change in seasons yearly, that some plants grow more during the rainy season versus the dry season. For example, there is the lime season in which the lime trees are filled with lime. There is the mango season in which the mango trees are filled with mangoes. There is the quenepes season in which the quenepes trees are filled with quenepes. The animals from the sea behave that way too. There is the red snapper season, the crustaceans season, and the baby whales season; these seasons are different because they denote migratory patterns and not growth in life.

CHAPTER 7

*J*ean now turned seventeen. He was planning on marrying Vernice the following year. He was finishing school. The family could not afford higher education for Jean. The grandfather gave him some sound advice. He advised Jean that the family would each put some money together for him to buy a piece of land. What Jean did afterwards was Jean's business. As in, he encouraged the marriage. Jean-Paul's philosophy in life was do what is best. According to him, if Jean did not get married soon, what would he end up doing? For example, he knows that Jean's dad never married. He didn't want that fate for Jean. If Jean found love, he was okay with it.

Some parents are strict and they feel that that is the absolute way to raise a child. Some parents are too strict, to the point that they have a military personality. Some parents are too easy going and because of their easygoing ways, their children fall into errors. Some parents like that of Sofiana are okay. They are not too harsh on their children and are always there to give a helping hand and some advice.

Jean-Paul reflected on Jean's life. His greatest fear is for Jean to follow in the footsteps of his dad, Joseph. He feared that Jean would father many children and worse yet, never take care of them. He always thought to himself that Jean would make it. He was impressed with Jean's attentiveness and curiosity when it comes to farming. At any rate, he was very happy that Jean was doing the right thing to Vernice and getting married. He was proud that Jean was being a man and not a child. For Jean choosing to marry and not lead a vagabond's life, it is said that Jean has earned his next hallelujah.

Jean started planning for his wedding. He went to propose to Vernice a year early. He went to her house to propose in front of her parents. Her parent's names are John and Marie. She had a sister named Martyse and a sister named Chanise . She had a brother named Huberto. She had an uncle who lived with them named Alexandre. Jean proposed and the family was happy with Jean. Vernice was also seventeen years old. Most people thought it would be a good match.

Vernice's family was protestant. Now here in the midst of a concentration of Catholics is a family of protestants. In the North of Haiti there are very few protestants. Most of them are located in Port-au-prince. This family went to church on Sundays, Wednesdays, and even on Fridays. One day Vernice asked Jean to attend church with her. He didn't mind so he went with her. He simply didn't know about the experience he was going to have there.

Jean went to church with Vernice. The name of the church was the The Cross Baptist church. At the door, everyone was very welcoming. They greeted him with care. In the church, Jean found the service loud and boring; he wanted to leave. When it was time for the sermon, Jean fell in love with the sermon. The sermon was about the prodigal son. The prodigal son is a sermon about how a younger son runs off with his inheritance. He wasted his inheritance into riotous living. Afterwards, he repented and he returned back to his father. His father accepted him with open arms and threw a party for him. After, this sermon Jean was changed. He thought about becoming protestant. However, he didn't want to disappoint his family. He mused over the sermon over and over. He didn't like the worship, nor the lengthy announcements, nor the prayers; however, he liked the sermon.

In regards to the prodigal son sermon, Jean started thinking about his mom: Sofiana. He wondered if he had been the prodigal son, would she have accepted him back. He wondered about his dad, Joseph, how he wasn't a father figure at all. Jean thought a lot about this sermon. It is this sermon that led him to accept Christ and become a devout Catholic Christian. Beforehand he was a Catholic who went to church for the sake of going to church; he was not a Christian. Sometimes, it doesn't pay to be too judgmental of one's fellow christians; it might just be a Christian from a different sect of Christianity that helps us get to the next level of one's journey.

Jean met with the priest of his church. He discussed the prodigal son sermon in detail with him. He asked about the father figure, if that was a representation of God. The priest answered that the father figure is a perfect representation of God: He is acting in love just as God would act in love. He then proceeded to ask the priests, how does one get born again in the Catholic Church? The priest froze and said that we don't particularly used the term born again. Catholics have their own process for those accepting Christ. Jean then asked him, if he could do it now. He said no to Jean. The priest mentioned to him that he would have to go to a set of classes. Afterwards, he would need to get confirmed. He went to church. He accepted Christ on the spot into his heart with a confession: a confession about believing that Jesus Christ is the son of God. One have to say hallelujah for Jean the mountainous man who was in search of Hallelujahs. He has chosen God as a seventeen year old. Afterwards, he talked about his familial relationship concerning his father; there was not a relationship between him and Joseph. He asked the priest for advice on how to deal with this issue because it really hurt him inside. The priest suggested forgiving Joseph as a first step. Secondly, meeting with him and having a talk. The priest said that he would arrange for the two to meet. Jean then went through his confirmation classes. After six weeks, he was confirmed as a Catholic Christian.

Weeks later, Jean decided to meet Joseph at a small restaurant titled Le Toussaint L'ouverture restaurant. Toussaint L'ouverture Is one of the founders of Haiti. The restaurant is modest with modest prices. As Jean was waiting at a table, Joseph busted in and yelled, "what do you want with me." Jean thought for a while and said maybe a father to son relationship. After all, you have time for two women and no time for your son. I would also like to take a DNA test to settle the matter of whether or not I am your son. If the test results fails, I will be out of your life forever. Joseph then said ok, I will step in and be a father. He then gave him a silly reason why he couldn't do it before. He blamed Sofiana. Jean simply rolled his eyes and didn't say a word. He said to Joseph, dad, there is a lot about you that I want to know. How about you tell me of your family history.

Jean-Bertho Almonord

Joseph started recounting his family history. Joseph's parents are name Alberto and Matilde. Joseph has two brothers named Jean-Claude and Jean-Remond. Joseph's family name is Riviere. Joseph has three other sons beside Jean that he knows about. Their names are Prospere Riviere, Sonie Riviere, and Jason Riviere. Joseph then thought about the fact that he hadn't given Jean his last name and remained mute. After much more talking, Jean told Joseph that he enjoyed this time together and that they should do it again in the future.

The family name of Jean's grandparent is Lapierre. His mom's full name is Sofiana Lapierre. She had a sister who was married. Her name was Jesula Lagrosiliere. Her husband's name was Andre Lagrosiliere. They had two children named Josue and Michel Lagrosiliere. They resided in the capital city of Haiti, Port-au-prince. The name can be translated to the Port of Princes. Sofiana had a sister who died at birth. Jean-Paul and Ana always remembered her. So they called her as though she were alive. Her name is Mythique Lapierre. Jean-Paul is also a grimeau in the Lapierre family.

On the way home, Jean met a girl who was visiting the area from Port-au-Prince. She stopped by saying "excuse me, Mr , I need help." He said "what kind of help." She said "I am trying to get to Ti Jean." Ti Jean is a voodoo shrine. He said "that is what you come to do here." She then retorted "justice must be served." She then asked him, 'are you really from around here." He answered her "yes, I am from the mountains." She then said, 'you mean you are a neg morne." Neg morne refers to any one who lives in the mountains. He answered not really, "I am a grimeau." She then started talking about neg marron. Neg marron is a folklore of Haitian history: he is an emblem of how the maroons who hid in the mountains played a part in the nation of Haiti. Her name was Theophine Biendone. She was a beautiful mulatress with long flowing hair. She said to him, "are you looking for a job", as in do you have an education. He responded that I am almost finished with my schooling. She asked him, "Do you want to be a teacher." My family has a school in Port-au-prince. He responded that I am a farmer. "Well farming pays very little in these parts and you can only feed your family." She said to him, "I will pay you if you take me to ti Jean." He decided to take her. On the way she started telling him of how she had two lovers who shall remain nameless. One was in love with her. The other was just playing her, but he had a wife. The wife found out and vouched to kill Theophine. Theophine pleaded and told her that she was not in love with him and that she is in love with someone else. The wife responded I do not care about love, I just need to pass enough people to make it. Theophine then told him that this is the reason she is going there. Once Theophine got to ti Jean, a grimeau bokor, voodoo lord, appeared and asked her for her cause. She spoke for herself. The grimeau bokor put up the hourglass of oil and said once this oil has finished dripping the person will die and that Theophine and Jean will have to consume their love. Jean froze and wondered what if Vernice found out. Theophine covered Jean's mouth with her hands so that he wouldn't talk. They went to a hotel and and slept together. In the middle of the night, they woke up and found themselves naked in a cemetery. They did not know what to do. Thankfully they weren't alone. Jean walked her back to the hotel and got their clothes and clothe themselves. Theophine thanked him and said if you need help when you are in are Port-au-Prince,

Jean-Bertho Almonord

don't hesitate to visit my address. Later on that day, the wife of the uninterested lover dropped dead.

On the way home, all Jean could think of is how he had betrayed Vernice, the woman he was supposedly getting married to. The first person he told was his grandpa, Jean-Paul. Jean-Paul gave him some sound advice. He told him that some time we go through trials and tests in life, to strengthen what is meant to be or not to be. He advised him to not live on a lie but to take the honest road with Vernice. However, he said be cautious, you might not need to tell her right away. Jean agreed. He said that I will get on my knees and pray before I go and tell.

Jean went to Vernice's house and recounted the entire tale. Vernice was shocked. She said this early on, things like that are happening. What about in the future. She then said next time, just tell these women no that you won't take them. She thought to herself for a while and said I forgive you. Jean was so happy to have heard these words. He rethanked her many times. She told him that I am getting married with you in a couple of months, that is my focus. Forgiveness is a powerful thing. It easily shields one from bitterness. In forgiving Jean for this silly mishap, Vernice had earned her first hallelujah.

CHAPTER 8

Jean turned 18. Before he turned eighteen, he invited his dad Joseph for one of those talks. He then invited him to the wedding. Jean graduated high school in Saint-Louis du Nord with honors. The name of the school was L'ecole Henri Christophe.

The wedding went as planned. Vernice was the most beautiful woman there. Her dress was pearly white. Everyone expected was there. The food was great. The music was good. So became Jean and Vernice man and wife.

Jean and Vernice went on their honeymoon in Port-au-prince. They stayed at La Belle Grimelle. During the honey moon Jean was very happy, but he realized that Vernice was not as happy as him. So he decided that he would tell her a joke. The joke is that a couple was on their honeymoon. They were a virgin couple: both female and male were virgins. They did not know what to do in terms of sex seeing that they had never had sex before. So the guy called his mom for help. She said to him lie on top of the girl private parts in tact, then put some corn on the guys buttocks, and tie a rooster placed it so that it can eat the corn. After lying down in tact, tap the rooster's feet. They obeyed the mom. The rooster started eating the corn and it's beak hit the guy's buttocks. The sexual motions started and the guy started whimpering in a low voice, give me more corn, give me more corn. The woman retorted the rooster needs more corn, not you. After Vernice heard the joke, she started to laugh heartily. The honeymoon went by more smoothly. At night, Jean and Vernice consummated their love, yet they used contraceptives. I think the whole idea is that they didn't want children yet. However, one would say that sexual love with contraceptives is not consummation. At the heart of contraceptives, lies a lie. A lie that hides the fact that marriage is for procreation; true consummation of love for the first time at least shouldn't entail contraceptives. If one is financially economically barren enough and one is christian, they can pray that the fertilization process does not take place. One can also pray that God helps them with his/her economic situations in order to be able to provide one's own children.

They moved in with Sofiana until Jean could get his own home. Jean-Paul paid for a piece of land in the mountains for Jean. Most of the money came from Jean-Paul; the rest of the family pitched in to buy the land as well. Even Joseph, who used to be an estranged dad, pitched in too. According to the work that needed to be done by the carpenters, it might take two months to put up a little house. Jean would of course be helping in the process. Jean did not have great carpenter skills; he wanted to hone those skills spying on and watching the workers.

It took roughly two months to build the house. It was a nice little house. It was a two bedroom house, which was very tight on space.

After the house was finished, Jean started to plant a garden. The first things he planted was a lime tree, an orange tree, a coconut tree, an avocado tree, plantain trees, and a papaya tree. He also planted roots, spices, and grains. He dug a well in order to get fresh water. He also went and bought chickens, guinea fowls, pigs, goats, turkeys, and cows. He bought both male and female in order to get them to reproduce. His hope is that the chicken would be producing so much eggs that he might be able to sell some of them. Jean was not a full time farmer nor a gardener, so he decided to go and look for a job with the carpenters. They accepted him. He was a nice guy, they said. We have to say for learning to provide for his family through farming, he gets an hallelujah. Furthermore, his grandfather, Jean-Paul, who taught him earns an hallelujah as well.

The family of two moves in. They are a happily married couple. Jean does the gardening and the yardwork; Vernice does the cooking and cleaning around the house. Vernice loved cooking. She loved playing around with her recipes; she loved improvising in her cooking. She cooks everything with garlic, even rice. She improvises all her food with spinach and okra, even rice. Things were tight for the two, but they were doing okay.

When it comes to the subject of Christianity, one would have thought that chaos would have erupted between Jean and Vernice's discussions. After all, it is an issue between a protestant and a catholic. Jean is catholic, meanwhile Vernice is protestant. Yet their discussions over the issue was not as rough. Vernice decided to obey her husband and become catholic. However, she bartered with him that sometimes the family can go to some protestant services. That idea pleased Jean. After all, having gone to a protestant church is what led him to accept Christ as a catholic; beforehand, he was simply not into God; He was simply existing, simply living his life. For Vernice obeying her husband in sincere christianity, she earned a hallelujah.

Vernice went through confirmation and accepted to become a catholic. It is funny that she became catholic after her wedding, which took place in a catholic church. She waited so long because it is a weighty matter. She had to see whether or not she is making the right decision. She had to go on her knees in prayer. She consulted her former minister. She explained to him that Jean was a sincere catholic christian and that she wanted to be an humble honest wife. The minister gave her sound advice such as that the wife should be in submission to her husband. The minister said to her that I know that Jean's heart is in the right place; I can also tell that he is truly born again. He said I do not trust a lot of catholics because they are simply going through the motions of going to church and are not born again. However,I trust Jean because I see that he is a catholic who is truly born again. Furthermore, I will speak to you a secret about him, I have a received a prophecy about him. The prophecy showed that he will rise to a higher level of success helping both catholics and protestants. For the minister instilling such a level of hope into Vernice about her marriage to Jean, we say hallelujah for a minister named Jean-Edouard Phillistin.

Vernice was worried about Jean a bit. There was the whole cheating scandal with Theophine Biendone. She easily forgave Jean because forgiveness was what she knew to do. She felt that she did not have any other options. However, in the back of her mind, she kept wondering whether or not he would repeat the offence. She kept wondering could her future be secure with someone who cheated before marriage. She never stopped to think about the negative effect of this thought pattern. He cheated before marriage; he might become a truly unfaithful husband. She did consider the fact that he didn't live behind a lie and hid it; he was honest. She knew of married couples that live behind a lie for so long that it led to their divorce. However, it felt good to hear what the minister said about Jean. It was confirmation that Jean was a good husband and that she had a creditable witness.

Vernice did not like going to catholic churches as much as she enjoyed going to protestant churches. She always felt that she was a protestant at heart. She loved the worship. She loved the prayer sessions. She loved the sermons, What did she like about catholicism? There were few things that she liked about catholicism. She thought the sermons were too short. She thought the worship was too short and not as lively. As for the prayer sessions, she felt that they did not have any. She did start to like confessions after she saw a confession of hope that helped her gain hope in life.

When exactly did Vernice accept Christ? It occurred shortly before the marriage. It occurred at the end of her sixteen years of age. She was living in sin as a teenager willingly sleeping around with Jean. It occurred after her great grandmother, Luciane, died. She reexamined her life. She was deeply saddened. She was raised with Luciane. Luciane was the one who always spoiled her with sweets. She played and doted on her all the time. After, Luciane's death, Vernice,s attitude on life changed altogether. She became a girl who was less interested about sex and more about God. At the funeral, the minister preached a sermon on how ephemeral life is. He preached that after death, there was hope for christians because they could go on to live with Jesus. That sermon set Vernice thinking about where she would go after her death, and then she accepted Christ. One can say hallelujah for a minister named Jean-Edouard Phillistin, who have led two sincere people to christ; albeit, one was led inadvertently. One says hallelujah for a mountainous woman named Vernice who chose God.

CHAPTER 9

Jean and Vernice were both twenty years old. They still did not have any children yet. Many people were skeptical. Some said that they couldn't have children. Some said that the infertility problem was with Jean. Others said that the infertility problem was with Vernice. Others waited to see the gorgeous children that would come out of their loins. Many people bombarded them with questions hinting that they needed a child.

Vernice wasn't sure as to how many children she wanted. She kept thinking around two. She always felt that children were a blessing and a reward from God. However, she always felt that too many children can lead to economic pressures. Jean, on the other hand, wanted only one child. He said being the head of the home, he always felt like too many children was an economic burden. Furthermore, he always joked that there is only one of him to go around. He can't spend the required time with each child, were he to have too many children.

One day Vernice and Jean planned a trip to Port-de-paix. At Port-de-paix they went to see Jean's cousin one generation removed, Merlande. Merlande lived at the heartland of Port-de-paix. She lived in a two story house. She lived with her mom, Marlene, Jean-Paul's sister. Marlene's husband's name was Henri. He was also the father of Merlande. Henri and Marlene had two children: Merlande, and Maribel. Merlande and Maribel were both younger than Sofiana. Maribel was the younger sister. Merlande was married to a guy named Luc Mirebalais. Henri's family name was Ceraphim. Merlande and Luc Mirebalais had one child. The name of the child was Philip Mirebalais. The child was ten years old. Merlande 's family like Jean's was also Catholic. Maribel had a son named Eugene. Eugene's dad was a white-American man named John Seymour. Eugene was a Haitian-American. Eugene Seymour was the same age as Jean; Maribel had him when she was young. He had double nationality. He was a dirty mulatto. In Haiti, mulatres that are not rich are called 'mulatres sales.' It literally translates to a dirty mulatto.

John Seymour went to Haiti on tourism. He decided that there were two cities that he absolutely wanted to visit: Port-au-Prince and Port-de-Paix. He might have been in love with both cities with ports. When he was at Port-de-paix, he became infatuated with Maribel. He went to a hotel with Maribel and they spent twenty-two days there. He obviously had money if he could pay for that many days in a hotel. Afterwards, he returned back to America and never came back. He didn't think that he was such a fertile man that he was leaving a son behind. He didn't think that he should at least be involved in the life of his progenitor. Maribel was also being foolish. She didn't stop to think what society would say about her after they found out. She didn't think about the hardship of raising a child out of wedlock. She didn't think about the economic hardships placed on a single mother. After all, many people think the races should intermingle; Mixed race children are usually very gorgeous.

The mentality of most Haitians is funny. They think that mulatres are the best looking. They think that the grimeaux are better looking than negs. Some believe that there are some good looking negs. Jean was not sure if they think that that hierarchy applied to education and intelligence as well. There are many negs that are educated who speak French fluently and command respect out of everyone. Some past presidents of Haiti have been negs. Many senators and congressman are negs. This mentality that Haitians have, is it a negative one or a positive one. It remains to be examined. Some Haitians have the worst inferiority complex; whereas some others have a superiority complex of the worst sort. Jean had a basic albeit shallow mindset about complexes; all complexes are a negative issue.

Port-de-paix was a thriving city with a port. One sees all the boats coming into the port with the merchandise. There was also the beach that people loved going to. There were the many little bakery shops, sweet shops, the butchers shops, and markets. Jean and Vernice walked around Port-de-paix as if they were tourists. Merlande and Luc walked along as well. They were impressed with the city. Some people pronounced the city Porde paix (as in with a french inflection), others pronounced it Port-de-paix.

On their way coming back from the city, the two couples saw a guy bathing naked on the street. Jean remarked to Vernice that you are staring too much at the guy. Vernice responded, no I wasn't cheri, maybe you were. Jean then responded that I was joking. She said me too. Merlande and Luc erupted in laughter. They both said that you guys are too much.

Port-de-paix is translated into english as the port of peace. Jean always wondered as to why a town would have such a name. As in, is there purpose in the names that Haiti give to its cities and town. For example, a town called a Port-of-peace is supposed to be a town with the most amount of peace. If peace is the absence of war, strife, and contention, then this town is supposed to be a haven for reduced crimes, reduced strifes, reduced contentions, and maybe even in reduced wars. Jean wondered how in Haiti's history has Port-de-paix played a role in shaping the peace of the nation or of the northern region.

CHAPTER 10

J ean and Vernice turned twenty two years old. At that age, a lot of things started to work out. Jean got a job teaching at the local school. It helped him earn an income. Vernice became pregnant and gave birth to a son. They named him Jean-Pasquale. He resembled both Jean and Vernice. That was a tender age to have children. Not only are most people opportunist, but most people are not mature enough to have children. Some people are in their seventies and haven't come to the conclusion that children are a reward from the Lord; they haven't come to the conclusion that if any one else's life is not sacred, the life of their own children are sacred. There are some things in life that people keep doing over and over again until they learn the appropriate and relevant lessons.

Jean and Vernice are always learning at least experientially. For example, Vernice doesn't only cook around the house. She takes care of the baby, which is a twenty-four hour job. She sows clothes for Jean. At the very best, they both try their best to make their home a happy home. Jean always thought about the difference between a house and a home. What is the difference between a house and a home? A house is something one buys, whereas a home is something one makes and build.

Jean received a teaching job at the local school. He loved teaching there. He taught elementaire 1. He was really intrigued about how the mind and the brain works. Some students seemed to pick up mysteries really fast; others picked up mysteries at a much slower pace. The favorite subject that he loved teaching was l'histoire D'Haiti. The Haitian education system is a didactic educational system; it has a didactic way of learning; the Haitians mainly learn through theory and memorization. The school does not have laboratories; it is not an applied learning environment. Jean and Vernice attended Sunday mass on a regular basis. They enjoyed the confessions. They even started to enjoy the sermons. They thought the worship could be improved. They usually talked to each other about the mass and how it went. They said that it was their familial duty to take their children to mass and grow as faithful catholics.

Meanwhile, on the side Jean and Vernice attended the The Cross baptist church that Vernice and her parents used to go to on the side; it was agreed in order to appease Vernice that the family could attend protestant services. Jean and Vernice always attended the baptist church on occasion. They didn't like everything there neither; however, both churches were a shelter to the daily ordinary life. Jean was very studious throughout the bible studies. He took copious notes. He went home and read them over and over again. He purchased a bible just for these bible studies. He purchased Le Louis Segond version de la Sainte Bible. It translates to Louis the II version of the bible. It is the most popular French version; it is comparable to the King James version of the holy bible. At a certain point, he started having personal bible studies with the minister, Jean-Edouard. He started having these bible studies when he was 19; they have been going on for three years. At this point, the minister asked him to lead Sunday school. He saw through the minister's ploy. He said that I am catholic and furthermore, I won't have time on Sundays. What I will I do is lead bible studies in my house with my wife and my child like the early church. The minister said I encourage that type of bible studies. Furthermore, I will continue studying with you until you get there in the faith.

Jean started leading bible studies. The bible studies that Jean led were becoming more popular. Half of those attending the mass started attending these bible studies. Furthermore, many baptist attended these bible studies. People loved studying the Word of God with Jean; He made it fun and interesting. He might not have been an expert on the bible, but the little bit he knew made him shine. Furthermore, these bible studies served as an enclave for protestants to meet with catholics and get over their differences; Catholics and protestants do share some things in common. Some of the topics that he covered was salvation, grace, and the prodigal son. For starting a Bible study group, Jean has earned a hallelujah. For getting protestants and Catholics to comingle, Jean has earned another hallelujah.

One time, Jean was leading a Bible study. There were about twenty two attendants. Twelve of the attendants were catholics; ten of the attendants were protestants. The subject of the bible study is the rapture. Jean was trying his best to do a resourceful study; as in people were taking notes and taking this study seriously. A catholic man, a newcomer, asked the question if the rapture is supposed to occur, why then do we go to paradise after we die? Jean did not know the answer off the top of his head. So he said that I am not sure of the answer, however I will look more into it. The guy was infuriated, he yelled, you mean I am wasting my time coming here. Jean apologized and asked everyone else if they felt that they were wasting their time and they said no. Jean then proceeded to say that if this bible study is too basic then study the Bible on your own. He then said, "I have another question for you, please describe the rapture." Jean for some reason started hyperventilating; everyone was shocked. Jean prayed a little prayer in his heart asking God for help. Jean said, " I am not sure why that question is of any importance; we are dealing with substance here." He then thought for a while as his thoughts cleared up. He then said I will describe the rapture to you. Everyone goes up to the heaven with a whirlwind. The questioner then said to Jean, unless you answered my question, I wouldn't have stopped asking you difficult questions. It is quite obvious he came to stir trouble. Halfway through the Bible study, he left. Everything returned back to running as smoothly as possible. For handling the situation with care, Jean earns a hallelujah.

Jean did not like to be made to look like a fool in front of his pupils at school, nor in front of his bible school attendants. It might be pride that causes him to behave this way; it might be his search for excellence in everything that he does that pushed him to behave in such a manner. At any rate, Jean reacted in a positive way; he started studying the Bible on his own with fervent ardor. He would read over a passage like two or three times in order to get the gist of it. Furthermore, he took copious notes while studying the Bible. Jean even got in the habit of memorizing a great deal of verses a day. Often times, it takes being tried by a ringer, before one find out the inner drive to excellency that he/she has. For reacting resiliently to a ringer, one can say that Jean has earned a hallelujah for his resiliency and and arduous study habits.

Jean and Vernice invited both of their parents and grandparents to the Bible studies. At first no one showed up. Later on Sofiana, Jean-Paul, and Ana started showing up. They were all very courteous. Sofiana felt bothered that she had to be there; she always wondered was this penance that she had to do for not going to church enough. Jean-Paul had high hopes in his grandson Jean; he expected to learn something each time. Ana was simply happy that she got some fresh air and that she was not at home.

At one of the Bible studies, Jean decided to teach on the prodigal son, the sermon that led him to accept Christ. He taught about how the father had a heart of forgiveness, how the father was like the God of more than second chances, and how the father was like the epitome of wisdom. After the teaching, he asked if any one wanted to accept Christ; two people accepted Christ. Jean-Paul and Ana both accepted Christ. It is funny how teaching works. It is the same sermon that led Jean to accept Christ as a catholic; it is a sermon that is efficient at winning souls. The family is strengthened that there are four christians in it. Furthermore, he gave Jean-Paul and Ana sound advice about what to do as christians. He encouraged them to keep coming to the bible studies. For getting both grandparents to accept Christ, Jean earns a double hallelujah.

Jean met Joseph on the way to work. Joseph asked him where was he going? He responded to school. Joseph retorted, school at your age. Jean responded, no, I teach at the school. Joseph then asked him, how did you land such a job? Jean responded through prayer. Joseph became angry and said, how did my son become a praying man? Jean responded, you would know, if we spent more time together, you would be more clued in to the details of my life. Joseph said to him, how about the meetings that we used to do, can we continue them?Jean agreed.

Jean was once in a bus going from Port-de-paix to Saint-Louis-du-Nord. He overheard two fellows talking. He didn't know their names. They were both about his color: they were grimeaux. They were saying something about robbing someone blind and then going to ti Jean to kill the person. Ti Jean is the voodoo shrine of justice; they were mocking what the shrine stand for. On the way, the bus tried to come to a halt, but it couldn't. It slammed into another bus. Someone on the bus yelled Jesus. Many others yelled Joseph, Mary mother of Jesus. It occurred so quickly that Jean did not yet have time to cry out to God; the effect of the conversation that he overheard had a hold on his attention span. Both mockers died in the bus accident, meanwhile everyone else lived. Some lived with a concussion. Jean had a minor concussion.

Jean-Bertho Almonord

CHAPTER 11

Jean and Vernice were now both twenty-six years old. Jean-Pasquale was now four years old. Jean started teaching Jean-Pasquale early on about the basics of life. He started with the alphabet and numbers at the age of three. He couldn't wait to teach him about farming and gardening. Furthermore, he told Vernice that I would like for you to teach our son how to cook. He told Vernice how he had learned how to cook by spying on his mom Sofiana and his grandmother Ana.

Recently, Jean had an idea about Vernice's cooking; it all tasted the same. She had been trying to cook rice, a staple that the family hate eating. She cooked rice with pinto beans, rice with mushrooms, and rice with black beans. They all tasted the same. Jean was worried when that kept occuring. So he told her that, before you cook any meal, pray over it. Little by little her hand started returning back. In Haiti, the majority of people in general are superstitious. They believe that a person's handwritings, his cooking hands, his intelligence, his memories, his eyesight, his intestines, gallbladder, and possibly even his private parts can all be stolen by an occultist never mind a master occultist. Jean and Vernice believe that was an attack on Vernice's hands. Many people say that occurs to them until they lose all mastery of cooking.

Jean-pasquale provided Vernice with some good company; she plays with him all day long. He is her pride and joy. He was a curious four year old. He was always quick to look, quick to ask why, and quick to learn. When children behave this way, especially at the earlier stages, it is a sign that they will go far in life. Jean-Pasquale behaved in a lot of ways like Jean when he was at that age.

Jean was asleep with his wife when he opened his eyes and he saw a death angel. Jean froze and wondered as to what to do. He made a quick prayer in his heart asking Jesus for help. He opened his mouth and asked the death angel who are you here for? He said, I am here for you, Jean. Then Jean said, who has sent you? He responded that I only answer one question. He grabbed Jean by the foot and just like this a death channel opened up and they were in hell. The death angel told him, you can pass a minister or a priest. Jean then said who sent for me? He said a person who you trust who wears a robe. The death angel then told him people are praying for you; as a result, please give the name of a minister that you would like to pass and I will return you back to your bed. Without hesitation, he said Father Michel. A black whirlwind appeared and Jean was back in his bed. Jean was extremely thankful. He got on his knees in prayer. He gave thanks to God for sparing his life. Jean then experientially knew what it meant that in the Bible that a threefold cord is stronger than a two-fold cord. If he was an asocial guy with no friends, an asocial guy who didn't lead bible studies, an asocial guy who was not married, he wouldn't have found any one to pray for him at the hour of his death. Jean had thoughts race across his head such as: who will raise my children, who will comfort Vernice, and who will lead the Bible study group after I am dead. On his knees, he cried to God that I am not ready to go, please allow me to see my son grow. He use to pray more than occasionally; however, this time around he knew prayer is powerful and it worked. For beating death this time and knowing where his priorities lie, Jean earned a hallelujah.

The next few days, Jean gained a profound respect for God, life, and family. He realized that without God no one can make it; he gained a complete trust and dependency upon God. He realized that life was a gift from God to be cherished and honored. He realized that his family was also a gift from God that he needed to steward. Jean was very wise; he didn't abruptly stop attending mass. In fact, he was leading three different bible study groups per week. A person had approached him and told him to consider going to seminary and applying for a parish license. He started going to a secret catholic seminary in Port-de-Paix two years ago; he was very close to getting his ministerial license. One day as Jean was worshipping in the Catholic church, he felt as if scales fell from his eyes and his eyes were opened and he saw that he was clothed in full white. He wasn't sure how it happened, but he was sure that he had become a saint. He saw Jesus standing in the center of the church with a piece of paper with Saint Jean Lapierre written on it. He had been taken from the league of those who give up too easily on God to the league of those who never give up on God. Hallelujah for a mountainous saint named Jean who was in Search of Hallelujah

In the Catholic tradition, it is the saints who uphold the church with Jesus. The saints are truly in a league of their own. They have earned their white garments. They pray and intercede for others in the church. They worship and give God the glory like no other. They are humble and they do not mind doing menial tasks such as cleaning the church. Under the auspices of Jesus, they look out for everyone in the church. They work with Jesus and God the Father. It is written in the Bible, to the saints of Ephesus. Hence, the affairs of saints, sanctification, or sainthood as the name goes is not only a Catholic affair, it is a biblical affair.

Two months later, Sofiana accepted Christ at one of Jean's bible studies. Jean was preaching on the role of Mary in the church. She was a chaste woman who chose the path of being a virgin not even knowing that she would become the mother of Jesus. The angel Gabriel gave her a high salutation, hail, Mary, full of grace, the Lord is with thee, blessed are you among women. Sofiana kept on thinking about the role of a godly mother; she felt that in a way or another she had failed Jean. She cried to God, have mercy on me a poor woman; I tried my best raising Jean. At the end of the service, Sofiana and her cousin Mariana accepted Christ. One say a double hallelujah for Priest Jean, the mountainous man; two more members of his family became christians. At this point, Jean became a minister/priest. He was not yet ordained. One say a third hallelujah for Jean for becoming a minister at the age of twenty-six. Most people become a minister at the age of thirty years old or older.

Jean's bible studies had been growing at a steady rate. As a result, he wanted to start a parish: an idea that is foreign to Haiti. Why is that? What is a parish? A parish is a church under the Catholic order where both protestants and Catholics can go to worship. In

Haiti, Catholics and Protestants simply do not intermingle. There are either Catholic churches or Protestant churches. Jean's parish became the first parish in Haiti. The name is La Paroisse de Saint Paul. It is translated to Saint Paul's parish after the well known apostle Paul, who was a leader in teaching sound doctrines in the church. Hallelujah for Jean, a pioneer, in starting a roundtable between catholics and protestants. A second hallelujah for Jean starting a parish. The Catholic order helped him purchase a building for his parish.

Jean waited eight months for the parish to finish building. It was beautiful. It had a statue of Saint Paul in front. There was a beautiful little garden of flowers by the statue. The parish was by no means as big as a cathedral, however it was as big as any ordinary church. As the parish was being built, Father Jean was in the business of looking for altar boys. He was also looking for a small choir.

One day he was walking into the parish, and Joseph followed him in. He was a little shocked. Joseph asked him what are you doing here? He replied to Joseph, dad, I am a priest here. This is the new parish in which I will host the masses for Protestants and Catholics alike. Do you know what a parish is? Joseph responded that quite frankly I don't know what a parish is? Jean then proceeded to say what a parish is. It is a church that allows a joint mass for protestants and Catholics that are in the body of Christ and they can fellowship together. He then thought for a while and he said, dad, do you want to also attend the bible studies that I lead. He said perhaps yes. Jean then asked him about the monthly dinners, are those still on? He then responded Yes. He left after afterwards.

Jean knows singularly that he has been wearing his father down. How so? He has been praying for him? He had not been praying the kind of prayers that are mean such as break dad's leg so that he would repent. Instead he prayed nice prayers over Joseph that God would protect him, that God would say a word for him, and that God would lead him in the light. Some people believe in prayers. Some people think prayers are worthless. Some people know that prayers are effective. At this point, Jean confessed that I know that my prayers are effective; my dad, a staunch sinner, has decided to attend my bible studies; his dad hadn't even accepted Christ.

Jean met with Joseph at Le Toussaint L'ouverture restaurant. They were talking about women, when Joseph said I am tired of taking you to this restaurant. I would like to go on a trip with you to Saint-Louis du Sud. On the way there, I would like to take an occultic stop with you. He then said that I know that you are a man of God, however, I did agree to attend your bible studies albeit begrudgingly. The least you can do is agree. Jean made a little prayer to God. He heard the audible voice of God speak to him giving him approval. He told his dad yes. Joseph frozed. Joseph said that I thought that you were going to say no. Jean said I can not let you down dad. Furthermore, he said to Jean there is a nice restaurant in Saint-Louis du Sud called Le Jean-Jacques Dessalines. He said that you do know who Jean Jacques Dessalines was. Jean mentioned yes. Joseph responded that he was a national hero who was a neg. A neg is a dark skinned Haitian. They have neg food. We can go in about two years. I need to get somethings in order before I go with you.

Jean-Bertho Almonord

CHAPTER 12

One time Joseph met Jean at Le Toussaint L'ouverture. Jean was now twenty-eight years old. He said that I want to reveal your lineage to you. I would also like for you to change your last name to Riviere afterwards. Joseph's grandfather was a French German named Joanis. He moved to the Haiti in search of riches. He had a Haitian concubine named Marie. They left Port-au-Prince and settled in the North of Haiti, specifically Saint-Louis du Nord. George, Joseph's dad, is the son of Joanis and Marie. He is a quadroon. However in Haiti, he is in the mulatres caste. Matilde, Joseph's mom, is a grimelle. She has one parent who is neg and one parent who is a mulatresse. Matilde's dad is the neg and his name is Mathieu L'enferriere. Matilde's mother waw a mulatress. Her name is Jesula L' enferriere. As it was foretold Jean in a dream by the evil spirits, Matilde died of cancer. George Riviere died before Jean was born.

Joseph finally showed up to Jean's door about going on the trip together. Some would dare say it's a route. Jean announced only certain particulars of the trip to his family. He had the trip planned around summer vacation so as not to miss school. He planned it starting on a Friday in order to make it back in time for Sunday.

Furthermore, he appointed someone to lead mass in case he didn't make it back in time.

Jean was not fond of taking buses. Yet, he had to go by bus to the destination with his dad Joseph. The last time he was on the bus, there was an accident; two people died who were going to ti Jean to resolve a matter; it is obviously the case that they were guilty; justice was served albeit in an occultic manner. Jean overheard them on the bus admitting going to ti Jean to kill.

Jean and Joseph caught the earliest bus at 6 AM. Jean brought some lunch and they ate on the way. They told jokes to each other. Jean told one joke in this manner with a shrilly voice. Imagine that magical beings are repenting and releasing people at will thinking it will please God the Father. Joseph laughed like a baby. He thought the joke was too funny. If anyone knows anything about magical beings,they know that they are beings that once they trap someone and hold them hostage, they never let them go. Joseph told a death joke about someone going to a funeral. He was crying for the deceased. Then the deceased appeared and said why are you crying. Stop crying. Go eat the well seasoned deep fried goat meat, pork meat, cow meat, and turkey meat. By the way while you are at it, leave some for me. The person froze, stopped crying and left the funeral out of fear. Jean froze and said do you mean the zombie. He then thought and said do you mean he faked his death and was eating with the guests. Joseph said, great job you got it on the second try. This joke started Jean thinking about a great deal of things. He started thinking about the art of faking one's death. He started thinking about what a zombie was and whether or not a zombie is alive. He started thinking about how ephemeral life is and about his own death. He paused and said with a smile on his face, it is not yet my time to go. Joseph smiled and said in his heart I had win my son. He thought to himself, years ago, I wanted to distance myself from him: even though I knew he was my son; I simply was not ready.

Joseph spoke to him about Christianity. He said to him, I go to church as a Catholic; yet, I am not a Christian. I do not go church as often. Furthermore, I am not a good person. I have multiple lovers. I sleep around. I even kill from time to time. I am not a gossiper because I am not a female. Jean said I get the point dad. Everyone on the planet, is a sinner. Everyone was born in sin. Everyone sins daily. Everyone will die in sin, unless the said person accepts Christ. What Jean was trying to say in sincerity is that God loves Joseph and so long as Joseph repented, God doesn't care.

They rode for a while on the bus. It was now 11 AM. They got out of the bus and took a camionette. A camionette is what one calls in English a tap tap. It is a little truck that is covered from the back. Many people can share the ride and pay as they get off. They got near a place called sceau d'eau. They went into a hotel and there they stayed until midnight. At midnight, they woke up and started their journey to sceau d'eau. It means the seal of water. There was a water fountain overflowing with water. Jean decided that everything he was told to do he would look up as a sign of asking God for permission. Jean, he said repeat after me, Neg kreol. Jean repeated neg kreol. A portal was opened. He said to Jean this portal connects Haitians to deepest Africa called Guinen, the home of the negs. Jean was then initiated into neg voodoo. He then said something else that Jean was supposed to repeat, tout grimo see moun.

He then motioned for Jean to repeat. Jean repeated tout grimo se moun. A portal then opened. He then said that this portal connects grimo Haitians to the deepest garden of Eden, where grimo ancestry started. He then said in German wissen Blut. Jean then repeated wissen Blut. A portal opened. He then said that this portal connects us to our white ancestry in which case mine and yours just happened to be German. The white blood when they connect to us, they sometimes feel sorry for us and look out for us, albeit selfishly. In one night, Jean was initiated into Haitian styled German, reg, and grimeau art voodoo. All three times, Jean looked up and didn't hear a word from God. Later on, it was the case that his father asked him, did you dance in the initiations. He responded Yes. It was so that his father informed him that I danced with you Jean. Sometimes later on you will dance with the devil as well and live.

Jean returned back to the hotel and he was upset. By upset, Jean wasn't angry, he was just unsettled. He was puzzled that he didn't hear from God the three times He looked up. Furthermore, he wasn't sure that this was a path that he wanted to take. To later dance with the devil put some fear into Jean. Joseph asked him what was going on in his brain? He lied and answered nothing. Joseph then asked, why are you so uncomfortable? He then said to Joseph, I have to be honest. I am a saint. I am not sure if sceau d'eau was the place for me. He then said Jean, I have other sons that are older than you. I have never picked them for this initiation because they are not saints. I will tell you something powerful about the occult, it always include saints for the good or the better of the saint. Furthermore, he said to Jean, life is what you make of it. Jean thought and said I am not supposed to be mad, we did have a pact that you would start attending the Bible studies.

Jean slept and saw that he was in the arms of God the Father. The father spoke to him and said that I had already spoken and told you that it was allowed. I don't need to respond three times in a row with a yes. You are shielding yourself by not praying and looking up, and I am supposed to answer in a circle where I don't have dominion. Jean, establish dominion. Furthermore, Jean asked am I still a saint. God responded that you are now a super saint, super saint Jean Lapierre or super saint Jean Riviere. God also responded to Jean, you should trust your father more. Jean then woke up.

The next day Jean and Joseph went for breakfast. They ate plantains and eggs. It was a hearty breakfast. Then they took a camionette back to the bus station. They did not get up so early this time. They left on a bus to Saint-Louis du Sud. Joseph was on the bus with Jean. He then asked Jean, ever wondered why some cities have similar names. Jean said I didn't. He then said it is probably because they have the same founder, or that they share something fundamental in common such as layout, or look. Jean said, that is interesting. I never thought of that. As the bus was entering Saint-Louis du Sud, he was shocked to see a similar structure: the entrance into the city. He looked for others as the day went on. They then went to eat at Le Jean Jacques Dessalines. The food was great. They enjoyed the food. Afterwards, they lingered around town until 6 PM. They then went to take the bus. The bus continued on its way to Port-au-prince. It was nighttime so they couldn't go sightseeing like they did at Saint-Louis du Sud. They shared a hotel room and the next day they took the bus on the way to Saint-Louis du Nord. Jean came back in time to resume his weekly affairs. The trip had only taken two days.

After this trip, Joseph had a different perception of Jean and life. Prior to this experience, he was not fond of Jean. He didn't trust Jean. In fact, he wanted to stay away from Jean. He dreaded the little meetings that they shared. Furthermore, he knew that Jean is a prayerful man who had been on his knees in prayer all the time; sometimes, he felt like running away from Jean and life altogether. It is apparent that he was afraid of Jean but why would he be afraid of life? He was afraid of life and was always running from life because he had a fear that life would catch up to him; as in, his past errors and mistakes would catch up to him. He felt that a distant cousin of someone he had killed would come and retaliate on him any hour. Many people feel this way about life; it is the essence of being superstitious. Now about Jean, Joseph felt that he could trust Jean a bit more; after all, trust is something that must be earned. He felt that he had won his son Jean back into his heart and into the Riviere family. The only thing is that Jean did not have the last name Riviere; he was working on changing that fact. Later on in the future, he decides to take Jean to the courts and changed Jean's surname; Jean is no longer known as Jean Lapierre; He is now known as Jean Riviere.

The workers had just finished building the parish. Jean was set to move in. Bishop Jean had an office in the back where he met with parishioners. Many of the protestants and the Catholics that he used to do bible studies with decided to join his parish. He had a parish of about 64 members. He applied to lead bible studies in the parish and it was approved by the Catholic order. Bishop Jean led the Bible studies on Wednesdays. Bishop Jean was now an ordained Catholic bishop. He could perform all priestly catholic rites.

It is now time to talk about Minister Jean's attitude as a bishop. He was very peaceful and jovial. He carried an air of being an erudite; he was not a totally learned man. He did not have a doctorate of philosophy nor of science; yet, he was learned in spiritual matters. At this point in time, Jean gained an ardor to read the Bible like at no other point in time. Jean decided to read the entire bible from beginning to end. He gained so much insight from reading the Bible. He then decided to read the Bible a second time throughout that same year. He loved worshipping. It is in this year, that Jean became a worshipper at heart. He loved the song, assembly worship the Lord; that was his favorite song. Jean grew in intimacy with God as a worshipper. One thing he always said to his parish is that worship is all about devotion to God.

One time Minister Jean was leading bible study, Joseph appeared. He was teaching on justification. Justification is the idea that christians are justified before God and are therefore not condemned. There are moments that are handpicked by God and this moment was one. Joseph silently shed tears in the middle of the teaching. After the Bible study, Minister Jean asked him, dad, why were you shedding tears. He responded because the message touched my heart. Minister Jean then led him to accept Christ. He confessed to Jean that I am not an honest man. I am addicted to sleeping around. I do a number of things wrong. However, I am willing to change. Joseph accepted Jesus Christ as his personal lord and savior. Bishop Jean had earned a hallelujah for getting his biological father to accept Christ. Joseph also earns a Hallelujah for accepting Christ.

CHAPTER 13

Joseph was sitting at a table with his son Jean at Le Toussaint L'ouverture. They were talking about just about anything. Then Jean said what about my brothers. I would like to see them. Joseph knocked his head backward and said that you know these brothers want you dead. I shield you from them. I refuse to bring them to see you because of their animosity toward you. Most of them have not done anything with their lives: yet, they blame you Jean. I have to say that the addiction to women issue they have, they got it from me. He then said to Jean, I have been meaning to tell you this. I never intended on being a faithful Christian after accepting Christ. I always wanted to be an unfaithful Christian. I am too addicted to sex. There are other dishonest things that I used to do that I have been reducing. He thought that Jean would have been judgmental. He thought that Jean's response would have been, not again or something. Jean listened intently. Jean then said God meets us where we are at in our journey.

Jean was now thirty years old. He had been in ministry for two years. Over these two years, his parish doubled in size. His parish had 126 parishioners plus the extra people, that were not parishioners, that came by to attend the masses. Many traditional catholics who visited the mass led by father Jean felt that it wasn't catholic enough. They felt that the sermons were too strong and that there was too much worship. Many protestants who visited father Jean's masses felt that it was too catholic. They couldn't stand the short worship especially the Ave Marias. They couldn't stand the sermons either; they felt that they were too strong. Both camps were in agreement about the sermons. However, the parishioners who accepted Christ truly saw it as true worship. They were happy to be fed spiritually by each sermon. For christians who are faithful, these little differences are inconsequential; serving God is always a heart matter issue.

Jean was talking to the priest of the Catholic Church that he used to attend. Jean was wise in a lot of regards. He knew it was the Catholic priest who sent the death angel after him. However, he still maintained contact with the priest. He talked with him on a regular basis. Some people would have been irate and confront the priest. However, that was not Jean's style nor does Jean recommend for anyone to behave in such a manner. Sometimes acting ignorant about matters that he/she is fully aware of is the best course to take on in life.

Similarly to the experience that Jean had with Joseph on the way to Saint-Louis du Sud, he had another experience with Joseph going to Gaspard. This time when Joseph mentioned it to him, Jean responded that there was no bartering that needed to be involved between him and Joseph; as in he is going without requiring anything. Furthermore, his dad comes to the bible studies enough according to Jean. Furthermore, his dad, Joseph, even accepted Christ because of Jean's bible studies. Gaspard is in the north of Haiti. It is situated between Le Cap Haitien and Saint-Louis du Nord. The trip takes about 45 minutes. They took a bus and they were there in less than an hour. They walked to a grimelle manbo's house. The name of the manbo was Jesula Selidieux. A manbo is a female voodoo lord. Joseph greeted her in a salutation that Jean did not hear. The manbo asked Jean what are you doing here. He responded that I am here with my dad. He knew that she was aware of his status as a saint. Furthermore, she then told them come along. They followed her into her house. She then asked Joseph, what is it that I can do for you dear. He said, that it is concerning my son. They both joked and laughed with each other as if they were lovers. She then say walk here Jean. Jean walked and he felt as if it was a force field entered into his heart. The stuff hurts. He was in pain. All he could do is yell. He started cursing. He yelled, Oh my fucking God what is this thing doing on me. He yelled , woy, woy, woy. He couldn't stop yelling, until the woman asked the loa on him to leave. Jean had finished dancing with a loa. A loa is a spirit that operates in haitian voodoo. Jean felt a sense of anxiety and unease; however he felt a sense of release and relief after the experience. The manbo then said to Jean, drink this. He saw a clear lucid drink. He drank it. His eyes and his senses then opened in the spirit realm to see mysteries of the occult. He saw several people standing by him such as Jean-Paul, Ana, and Sofiana, even Vernice was there with the child. Vernice looked at him and said I love you dear but I need to protect my family and children; It is the primary reason why I can't achieve sanctification. The manbo said to Jean look to the left. Jean looked and he saw himself dead and buried in the grave. She said look to the right. Jean saw himself clothes in white with a legion of angels behind him; he was saying in Haitian Creole, Ou pap pase. The saying translates into English as you will not pass. He saw in front of him Baron Cemitieres, Baron Miniut, and Baron Samedi full with snakes all over them and both of them with an army of fallen angels behind them. Baron Cemitieres is the one in charge of the kingdom of death in Haiti. Baron Samedi is the one in charge of the underworld. Baron Miniut is the one in charge of the night. She then drank some rhum. She spat on the ground. She looked up. She looked down. She said look in front of you. He saw Joseph almost dying of cancer. He then asked dad, do you have cancer. He responded yes, one of the worst kind. I was afraid to tell you Jean. The manbo said to Jean that you haven't been keeping up. Instantly, he knew what she was talking about. He said he hadn't been keeping up. She stripped him off his clothes made him bathe in an unction having coconut water and avocado. He then was made to jump over the voodoo fire and over a skull seven times. She said to him in a strange creole language, ayibobo, neg a konn koke aswe. He froze. Ayibobo is secret African phrase that Haitian occultist say. Most people do not know what it mean. One can say ayibobo for the manbo; As in, good job to the manbo. After he had heard the manbo, his wife looked at him and said with me. He said yes. He then was relaxed. The manbo said this guy will be having sex tonight.

The experience that Jean had with Joseph lead Jean to reflect deeply over his life and life in general. He never knew that his wife Vernice went to this places. He wouldn't dare call it a double life, because he is more mature. He just felt that he should have known. His child was being brought to these places as well too, he thought. One need to remind Jean that he too as a child came to these kinds

Jean-Bertho Almonord

of places with Sofiana. After he thought of that experience, he cooled down; he had forgiven Vernice. He knew that she was doing it for protection. Yet, he wanted her to count on God. Haiti is a nation that is strong in the occult; as a result, many Christians refuse the faithfulness route; they would rather have protection from the occultic forces rather than from God.

Jean was musing on the visions. The first vision was of him dead and buried. He didn't even ask the woman who buried him alive. He was struck by the vision. He knew it was real. So he decided to go to God in prayer. He didn't ask God who did that to him? He simply went in prayer. The second vision was even clearer. It is clear that he is the one giving the family protection through Christ; A praying saint in a family helps against a number of things. The third vision depicted that Joseph had cancer. Jean was not yet a saint that believed in healing. Yet he desperately wished that there could be something done for his dad. What a mishap when a Christian does not believe in healing. However, Jean had heard someone briefly talk about healing and that God does miraculous healings still today.

According to Jean, prayer resolves many things. He went to God in prayer for Vernice and his son, for Joseph in general and the cancer, for protection for the entire family, for his brothers from Joseph's side who didn't like him, for Haiti, for Saint Louis du Nord, for his parish, and for the saints. Two weeks later, Jean received news that his dad's cancer was partially subsiding. Jean's faith grew. He started to remember the fact that he had been reading the Bible from start to finish. He remembered some passages that talked about healing. He decided to do a topical study on healing in the Bible. He found a wealth of information to be studied. Hopefully, he will start operating in healing.

Jean was talking to Vernice. He said to her, what do you think about the second vision that I saw. I was defending the family. Don't you think that this is a sign of me granting the family protection through Christ. Vernice started to cry. She responded, Jean, I don't know why I can't get myself to completely trust God when it comes to protecting my family. My entire family goes to these places to seek protection. You are the only who doesn't go to them. When I saw you there? I froze. I didn't want you to see me. Jean said, it is okay Vernice. I have forgiven you. She said thank you. I will however ever pray that you will grow in Christ and start to trust God more. Two weeks later Vernice became a saint. The family consisted of two saints. A triple hallelujah goes to Jean. One hallelujah for understanding and not scolding Vernice. A second hallelujah for praying more and getting his dad a partial healing. A third hallelujah for getting Vernice to the level that she became a saint. After two months, the number of saints in the parish jumped from one to seven. A fourth hallelujah goes to Jean for more than doubling the number of saints of his parish.

CHAPTER 14

Jean was now thirthy-one years old. His son, Jean-Pasquale, was now nine years old. Vernice was also thirty-one years old. Jean-Pasquale was very precocious; he learned things very quickly. His mental acuity was very swift. Jean walked to school with him every morning. Whereas the latter was going there to teach, the former was going there to learn. At home, Vernice spent a good amount of time reviewing Jean-Pasquale's homework with him. Vernice always had high hopes for Jean-Pasquale. She dreamed of him one day leaving Haiti and going to America for university. America was a powerhouse for technology, education, and knowledge. The most accomplished and famous universities were there such as the Massachusetts Institute of Technology, Harvard University, and Yale University. These universities are expensive but she thought with God's help and possibly some scholarships, that Jean-Pasquale could make it to one of these universities. She started talking to Jean about it. Jean said that I never thought about it. I am going to test him for a more advanced track in school.

The following day, Jean-Pasquale spent two hours in school getting tested. Two hours later, the proctors and graders of the tests reported the results. Jean-Pasquale received a 10 on everything. He was certified to skip one grade level subjected that his parents approved. Jean and Vernice approved. Jean-Pasquale was no longer in elementaire 1, but elementaire 2. He was a nine year old in class with ten and eleven year olds. Jean watched the progress of Jean-Pasquale with amazement. Jean-Pasquale adapted quite well to his new class room and studies. He said to Vernice that within six months we can schedule him to be further tested.

Jean had been working on some studies of his own. From the last time that he had read the Bible entirely, he had read it two more times; he had read it for a total of three times completely. This time around, he started studying the Bible as he read it. He was particularly researching the subject of healing. He had at least eight solid scriptures on healing. He was working a teaching and a sermon. At this point, he started teaching with proofs. A proof entails two or more backup scriptures that gives an explanation as to why something is true or as to why it works. Every sermon or teaching that he taught or preached from this point forward had at least one proof. People started intently listening to his sermons to the point a man asked him would he like to be on a catholic radio station for thirty minutes a week. He agreed. He didn't have to pay anything. It was sponsored by the catholic order.

Jean was once writing his biblical notes and then he had a vision of God. He was in heaven. God started talking to him about healing. God said that it is my desire to heal everyone. However, most people are in ignorance concerning healing. Even you, a faithful Christian, do not know what healing is. He said to Jean, take eat this scroll. He ate the scroll and then realized that he had a revelation of healing. The vision ended. After this point, Jean knew exactly what he was supposed to do in terms of healing. He meditated on the healing scriptures a heck of lot more. He taught four teachings on healing in four respective different bible study groups. Afterwards, he preached a powerful sermon on healing. Three persons walked down the aisle and he prayed for them and they got healed. It was one of the first miraculous healings to be done in Saint-Louis du Nord. There are reported cases of healing in Port-au-Prince though.

Jean was always worrying about his dad, Joseph, whether or not he would live; his cancer was strong. Jean's faith grew after the two miraculous healings. He walked to see his dad. He prayed over his dad while citing healing scriptures. Joseph retorted I didn't feel anything. I am not sure if I am healed. Jean said that at the church everyone who asked was healed. I am not sure what happened and why it didn't work.

Jean said that I will continue in prayer. Typically, Jean would have been mad, sad, and confused. However, this time he said I need to figure out why it didn't work. The difference is that he gained a revelation that healing is for today.

Early in the morning the next day, Joseph was in front of Jean's door. He resembled a rejuvenated young man. Jean froze. Jean jumped up and down. He yelled for Vernice. He said to Vernice look at what God has done. God has healed my dad of cancer. Joseph said thank you son for praying for me. I was losing hope in life; I am not even that old; yet, now I have the joy of living; I desire to be reconsecrated and follow God in faithfulness. Afterwards, Joseph became devoted to God out of love and his sexual addiction left. After two months, Joseph became a saint; sanctification and serving God requires devotion. One can say that the mountainous saint named Jean had earned another hallelujah for his belief in healing. Jean deserves a second hallelujah for getting his dad, Joseph, to choose faithfulness. Jean deserves a third a hallelujah for leading Joseph in the path of sanctification. A praying saint is a powerful saint; prayer always works; prayer can be hindered or delayed, but it always works in the long run.

After six months, Jean-Pasquale was tested again. He passed the test verily easily. He received 10s on everything. He was promoted to a higher level class. He adapted well to the class work and the social atmosphere. Jean gave God praise and said hallelujah to God the Most high that I have raised such a precocious and handsome son. He asked Vernice to do the same. She repeated Hallelujah to God the Most high that Jean and I have raised such a precocious, handsome, and obedient son.

CHAPTER 15

J ean was now thirty-two years old. His radio program was doing well. People loved listening to him. It had been on the air for a good nine months. He talked about important and relevant issues such as prosperity, healing, raising children, Bible reading plans, abortion, homosexuality, and other bible teachings in general. He even did sessions in which he told jokes. The show had a record number of listeners. The head of the radio program came to him asking to increase his program to a five days a week thirty minute program. Jean agreed but he said I needed approval. The Catholic order approved of the payment. Jean was then on the air on a weekly basis.

Jean started going through a series of attacks and persecutions. He would be inside his house with his son and wife at night, all of a sudden he would hear birds falling on the roof. He was not sure of what to do. He prayed with his wife. Yet the persecution increased. He spoke to his wife Vernice. Vernice said to Jean that I might not be a powerful saint like you, but I am not going backward in dealing with voodoo Lords. Jean said to her that I was not asking you for that. Later on that night the back door was opened and a black cat walked in and jumped into Jean-Pasquale's bed.

Jean-Pasquale was asleep, yet everyone heard him screaming and yelling. Jean woke him up. Jean asked him what happened? He cried and said that he was having a nightmare. In the nightmare, two black hallow figures were chasing him. After a while, he looked and he said where did that black cat come from. Jean said get out to the cat. The cat ran outside and said a meow. Jean-Pasquale then went to sleep with his parents. That entire night, the Riviere's house was under attack. About a thousand black birds fell on the roof with a loud thump. The main purpose of such an attack is that the person being persecuted will not get any rest.

The next day Jean went to look for Joseph to talk about the persecution. He found Joseph. He explained what took place to Joseph. Joseph paused for a second and looked and then said, what do you want me to do? He paused and said nothing. Joseph then said, good, because I am a saint now. I can not do the things that I used to do. Jean then responded, can you give me an interpretation? He then looked up and down and said no. Jean was puzzled; so he left.

The next day he went to Jean-Paul. He asked Jean-Paul the same question. Jean-Paul gave him the same answer. Jean-Paul responded what do you want to do. You know obviously that I am not a saint. He said once again, I just want some kind of explanation. You are my grandson Jean-Paul said, it is my duty to look out for you. You are under an all out attack from a number of wizards. They want you dead for the work of Christ that you are doing in a predominantly wizard neighborhood. I could give you this information because as a christian, I get help from God. Jean-Paul however told him that it is not only your father Joseph that need to do routes with you. I need to do one with you. Being a bit more shrewd, Jean decided to barter with him. Jean-Paul agreed to come to more bible studies and to listen to the radio program. He then said grandpa, what do you think of Jesus? Is he savior to you or not? Jean-Paul said that he is my savior; however, I simply do not respect christianity. I see saints dying in the hand of wizards all the time; I don't intend to be one; furthermore, I need to protect me and my family. They then scheduled a date next week for the route.

The following week they took a bus to Cap Rouge. They walked a few blocks to a house. They saw a bokor and a manbo. A bokor is a male voodoo Lord. A manbo is a female voodoo lord. They both bowed down to Jean-Paul. However, they said to Jean, salut monsieur. This means greetings Mr. They told Jean-Paul follow us please. Jean-Paul then motioned for Jean to follow. Jean promptly followed. In the house, there were skulls everywhere. Jean was a bit scared but not overwhelmed. Jean-Paul then said the word ayibaba ayibobo. Seven spirits of the dead appeared. He then slipped into an Haitian voodoo chief's outfit. He said to Jean that I am the presiding voodoo lord here. I am a phony of phony Christians. I don't trust God. I am simply using God. He took the skulls and grinded it to a powder and he said taste it. Jean then tasted it. He then took some blood and said to Jean, drink. Jean then drank it. He then said go jump through the voodoo fire seven times. Jean jumped through the voodoo fire seven times. Jean then looked and he saw the number of saints that his grandpa was holding hostage and he swallowed his saliva in fear. His grandpa said what did you see. He lied and said nothing. He then taught him seven voodoo prayers. He gave him seven handkerchiefs. He then recited his name in Kreyol and said Ou se Ayisien, pa jue avek mwen. It is translated into English that you are a Haitian, never play fresh with me. He then said you are now a Voodoo Lord? He then spat on his face. He said, this is for making every moron mock the family. Jean responded thank you. It is certain that Jean-Paul was bitter. Jean had to force himself to remember that this was the Jean-Paul who raised him and who taught him wisdom. Jean left and went back to his house. On the way home, he kept asking God what do I do with such a right. He thought about renouncing it after prayer in his house. As he was walking he had a vision. He saw Jesus walking toward him. Immediately, he knew it was Jesus. He then said master, what do I do with such a right. Jesus said, keep it. You need it for redemptive rights. You need to learn how to bind it. He flustered and said, you mean christians can operate in this kind of power. He said of course. All power comes from heaven. He said thank you Jesus, you have comforted me. The vision ended.

CHAPTER 16

Jean was now thirty-three years old. The age thirty-three is typically referred to as an age of suffering. It is the age in which Jesus died on the cross. On the day that Jean turned thirty-three, he found out that both him and Vernice had cancer. They had both been suffering from tremendous pains. Their skins felt like it was burning. They were both praying saints. They decided to go on their knees in prayer. Jean one day spoke healing to both his cancer and Vernice's cancer. Jean's cancer subsided but Vernice's cancer lingered on. Jean was fearful. He did not know what to do. He prayed a second time and the cancer did not go away for Vernice. He cried to God the third time and did not hear a voice. His lamentation was that Vernice is a mother. She is a faithful servant of God. She deserves to see her children live. She has not even reached her fifties. He did not hear anything from God. He decided to take her to the hospital. She was diagnosed with stage five lymphoma. She was given one month to live. At the hospital, they took good care of her.

When Jean-Paul found out about the cancer. He yelled at Jean like a baby. He said, I don't know why you serve this God of yours. I will sooner renounce my faith so that my daughter-in-law lives.

The wizards want to eat your wife and you are sitting there praying. By this point in life, Jean was a more mature saint. He said I didn't know you felt this way. He took Jean-Paul and Ana to see Vernice. At the same time he took Vernice's parents to see Vernice.

Vernice cried to her father-in-law as well as her father not to do a route. She then said that she would rather die a martyr's death than to return back to the occult. Vernice's father froze. Jean-Paul froze. Jean-Paul yelled at Jean, this day I renounce my faith because of what my daughter in law had said. Ana then looked at him and said I was never a christian. I muttered curse God and die when I accepted Christ. Both of them said, you are doing this route with us and that is final. Jean responded Yes.

As Vernice was on the hospital bed, she had a vision. Seven angels descended and said to her your cries as well as your husband's cries have reached God. We are impressed that you have chosen martyrdom over the occult; this behavior pleases God; however, you are not called to martyrdom. It is because of that we have decided to come down and heal you. Vernice felt an intense rush of clean water running throughout her entire body. She woke up and just like that she was healed and she thanked Jesus; meanwhile, she had forgotten the vision.

At midnight that night, Jean, Jean-Paul, and Ana went to do a route. They approached a house and a servant girl said, you guys may enter. Jean saw a bokor waiting for them. The bokor took some water and said step in it Jean. Jean obeyed. He then said, isn't it weird that you have stepped in water? Jean said yes. He then said a life for life is the rule of death. If you don't pass someone, you will be passed. Who do you want to pass? Jean thought and said to himself, couldn't my life get any harder. He prayed to God and God did not answer. He looked up and he looked down and said the person who buried me alive. The person who buried Jean alive is a nasty occultist by the name of Jacques-Marie Louis, a cousin of Joseph from his mother's side. Within three days, Jacques-Marie died of cancer.

Afterwards, Jean wondered if he did the right thing. If the hands of God were upon him. He was extremely happy to have found his wife alive and well. He never believed that it was the voodoo lord who healed her; he believed it was God. One day he went home and he found his wife cooking some strange meat. He didn't know what kind of meat it was? It was some deeply fried meat. He tasted it and said it was good. His wife looked up at him as his eyes opened to see into another realm and said, now you are a Voodoo Lord. He was amazed. He said to her, how do you know these things. She said, you think the daughter of a voodoo lord doesn't know these things. She then said, I might have become a faithful christian, however I haven't lost what I used to know. My dad's name was Jean-Robert Clemeste. My mother's name was Delila Clemeste. My dad was a faux-grimeau. My mother was a mulatresse's. I am their child: a grimelle. When the cancer struck me and I couldn't be healed, I thought it was their iniquities that was following me. I have never shared that story with you before that he was a voodoo lord. I had never given you their real name. It is not because I do not trust you. It is simply because I was guarding family secrets. My father was one of the worst occultist in Haiti. He used to kill saints and people's children for fun. It wasn't until he met his match Jean-Paul that he ran and made the entire family become protestants; he was seeking godly protection. Even before we started dating in school I knew that we would have gotten married. I was sold to Jean-Paul, your dad, as a consolation prize. One says that Vernice has earned a hallelujah for being a mountainous wife who showed her husband the art of the occult of turning someone into a peon.

There are those who say true repentance into Christianity is a heartfelt matter. There are those who say that saints who used to be in the occult and have deep knowledge of the occult and are truly repentant makes the world go round. Jean knows that both statements are true. He now holds his wife in a much higher regard and respect. He in turn decides that I will give her the benefit of the doubt most of the time.

Jean-Pasquale was now eleven years old. He was still bright as ever in school. He was very obedient to his parents. He liked going to church. He loved worshipping God. He also loved playing the guitar. He did not know that much about the occult. He just remembered that he used to go to occultic meetings with his mom. It came to a stop after he saw his dad in one of the occultic meeting. He was due for his next advance track exam. He passed the exam verily easily. He got above 9.5 in everything. He skipped one grade level again. He was now in moyen 1 as the title of the grade level. These students were twelve and thirteen, and most of them looked at him as a peon: a smart little peon.

Jean's radio show was doing well. He was now on the air five days a week for thirty minutes; the ratings were up as well. A number of people loved his show; even a number of occultists loved listening to him. It was very surprising what he talked about. He talked about ordinary issues in a relatable way. Many people recorded his shows and listened to them over and over again. One time he was taking calls live. An occultist called and said you fucked up wizard, keep up the bullshit, and see if your son won't be dead and eaten. Wizards need to live too. I give your son two days to live. Everyone who was listening froze. Some people started praying for him and his son instantly. After the recording, he went straight to his son's school and took him home.

At home, he started consecrating his son and praying over his son, Jean-Pasquale. He taught Jean-Pasquale how to pray. He taught him how to ask God for help in trying circumstances. He then asked God to open Jean-Pasquale's heart in order to be receptive to the Word of God. He taught him a teaching on the story of the prodigal son. Jean-Pasquale cried after the story and accepted Christ. He looked up to the heavens and said thank you Jesus that my son is saved and that he has accepted Christ. Furthermore, thank you for answering and hearing my prayer. He taught Jean-Pasquale twelve worship songs. He then asked Jean-Pasquale, do you have any questions. Jean-Pasquale responded, what are angels. Jean responded that angels reside in heaven; they make up God's army that comes and help humanity when christians pray or worship. Furthermore, he said that every child has a guardian angel who watches out over them. Jean-Pasquale grew spiritually and grew in reverence of God. It is ultimately a thing of beauty that Jean started to work on his son's spiritual education; it shouldn't have waited until this battle. Hallelujah for Jean for getting his son the ultimate protection in life : salvation. Hallelujah for an obedient son who Revere's God and desires to learn the things of God.

Two days later, Jean-Pasquale was found lying dead in his bed. Vernice started crying. She kept saying, our son, our son. What am I going to do. Oh God, please say a word for my son. She then had a vision and seven angels walked into the room. They said be still and know that God is powerful. Jean rushed down from his sleep and said what happened. He hadn't seen the angels. He however felt a godly presence and was comforted. The moment Jean came, her memory triggered and she remembered the vision she had at the hospital. Jean prayed over Jean-Pasquale and said in the name of Jesus, arise. Jean-Pasquale rose from dead. Vernice's tears changed from a sorrowful tear to tears of joy. She said I worship God forever and know that he is a powerful God. Jean then said that we have the victory over the wizards, I have to announce it on the radio. Vernice looked puzzled and said to him, what haven't you learned about wizardry? He then smiled and said I am learning a lot about wizardry. He then told Vernice and Jean-Pasquale about the dare.

The same day he went to the radio station and publicized the matter. It was a dare from the pit of hell against Jean and his family; Jean prevailed; his family chose God and the person who died was brought back to life; the wizard did not kill and eat Jean's son. Many christians called in solidarity and said congratulations. Many others said that they will keep him in their prayers. Many others cried tears of joy with him. There were even some occultists who sympathized with him. The ratings of the radio program boomed. Many people were beyond impressed that in Saint-Louis du Nord where wizardry reigned, there was now a saint who could raise the dead back to life. One says that a mountainous saint had earned another hallelujah for operating in the resurrection of the dead.

CHAPTER 17

Jean-Pasquale excelled in school so much that his father, Jean, began to be worried. Soon enough, Jean-Pasquale was starting to act up. He was starting to hallucinate. He was starting to hear voices. Jean-Pasquale didn't know what was occurring to him. However, his parents knew exactly what was occurring to him. They presumed that the other children were jealous and they told their parents. Their parents in the other hand might have retorted to voodoo. The reasoning is that you might as well go insane since you are so smart. Being two praying saints, Jean and Vernice decided to go on their knees in prayer. They prayed all night and interceded for their son. In the morning, God impressed something upon their heart. God impressed that Jean-Pasquale would be sick for four years. He would have to miss school for four years straight. Afterwards, he would recover and complete his studies. They both thanked God that their son would live.

Years later, Jean-Pasquale, had his last set of exams scheduled. he took the exam with excitement. He passed the exam with all tens. He now was placed in the senior graduating class called the baccalaureate. He had to start applying to universities. Jean started reviewing the application process with Jean-Pasquale. He mailed letters asking for brochures of certain schools from the office of education. He sent them a transcript and asked for recommendations of universities. They responded with several schools in America and one school in Haiti. They gave him an advice of applying to multiple schools; it might be the case that one gets rejected from his/her favorite school. There was one school in particular that struck Jean-Pasquale's attention : the Massachusetts Institute of Technology (MIT). Why did it strike his attention? The school is a math, science, and engineering power house. Jean took his son Jean-Pasquale by the hand and said let us go to God in prayer. They prayed that Jean-Pasquale's desire would be granted. They prayed that God would help him excel at whatever school he desired to attend. After the prayer, they both felt that they were comfortable with Jean going to university. Vernice and Jean knew that God would be watching over Jean-Pasquale; He would be starting university at the age of seventeen. Jean-Pasquale definitely applied to MIT and several other schools. He was later on accepted at MIT.

Jean's thought kept reverting back to the past vision that he had at the manbo's place. He had the vision that he was buried dead underneath the ground. He decided to resolve that vision once and for all. He prayed a sincere prayer in which he said Thank you Jesus that you restore my soul and resuscitate me from the dead. After that he had a vision given to him by God. He saw that he was dead and buried under ground in multiple places. He was shocked. He was thirsty so he decided to go for some coffee. He took some coffee and drank it. Afterwards, he saw all the different pieces of his soul springing back to life and being restored. When he awoke, he went in prayer and thank God. God then spoke to him in an audible voice and said do it for your family too. He then went in prayer and prayed for his family concerning this matter. This shows that certain prayers need to be specific.

Jean's radio program grew to the point that he got investors. The program was lengthened from thirty minutes to an hour, five days a week. With the investors investing into the program. Bishop Jean was now getting an annual salary for his radio program. The radio program remained just as relevant. Jean gained a wide range of followers. At this point the program became more structured. Some days were dedicated to prayer, whereas other days were dedicated to worship. Some days were dedicated to political issues, whereas other days were dedicated to jokes.

Jean's lot in life increased dramatically with the salary that he was now receiving as a radio host. At first, he was thinking that it would be impossible for him to pay for Jean-Pasquale's higher education. He went to God humbly in prayer and said that even us christians need an education. However with the promotion at the radio station, he became prosperous enough that he could pay for his son's education; it is a blessing to be able to afford and pay for one's children's higher education. Jean contacted the university about ending the scholarship; he paid the rest of the tuition with his own money. Furthermore, Jean started investing in his community. He opened a little farmer's market, where the farmers come and trade their produce. The market was very prosperous. He was then promoted to be the principal of the school where he taught. He visited America for the first time in the year 2019. He was shocked to see how beautiful the country was. He thought that MIT was one of the best looking universities. He felt that the school was huge. This is probably due to the fact that he is from the provinces of Haiti. He saw how huge the Haitian diaspora living in America was. He then opened three restaurants: one in Saint-Louis du Nord, one in Saint-Louis du Sud, and one in Port-au-Prince. The restaurants all go by the name: la grimeauxianie. He became truly prosperous. If there aren't any other prosperous Haitians, here lies the case for a prosperous Haitian who was Christian. For achieving a prosperous Christian Life and investing into his nation, and even America with the education of his son, one says that Jean, the mountainous man, has earned a powerful hallelujah.

ABOUT THE AUTHOR

Jean-Bertho is an author who was born in Haiti. He came to America at the age of ten. He graduated from the Massachusets Institute of Technology (MIT) with a joint bachelors in Electrical Engineering and Computer Science. He worked several years as an engineer. He became an author at the age of 37.